PO PIANO
AND KEYBOARDS
ENTRY ZONE ➤ *Debut*

A *Rockschool* Publication
Broomfield House, Broomfield Road, Richmond, Surrey TW9 3HS

Welcome To Debut *Popular Piano*

Welcome to the Rockschool *Popular Piano and Electronic Keyboards* Debut pack. This pack contains everything you need to play popular piano in this grade. In the book you will find the exam scores in standard notation with fingering suggestions. The CD features performances of the tunes (with no digital edits) to help you learn the pieces. There are also ten practice ear tests. Handy tips on playing the pieces and the marking schemes can be found in the Guru's Guide on page 10. If you have any queries about this or any other Rockschool exam, please call us on **020 8332 6303** or email us at **office@rockschool.co.uk** or visit our website **http://www.rockschool.co.uk**. Good luck!

Entry Zone Techniques in Debut and Grade 1

The eight Rockschool grades are divided into four Zones. Debut *Popular Piano and Electronic Keyboards*, along with Grade 1, is part of the *Entry Zone*. This Zone is for players who are just starting out and who are looking to build a solid technical and stylistic foundation for their playing.

Debut: in Debut you will be concentrating on playing tunes. A player of Debut standard should be able to play up to 16 bars of music in either 2/2, 3/4 or 4/4 time, using simple melodies composed of semibreves, minims, crotchets and associated rests.

Grade 1: in this grade you should be able to play up to 20 bars of music using melodies composed of semibreves, minims, crotchets, quavers and associated rests.

Popular Piano and Electronic Keyboards Exams at Debut

Players wishing to enter for a Debut *Popular Piano and Electronic Keyboards* exam need to prepare **five** out of the six pieces contained in the book. Each piece is marked out of 20, making a total of 100 marks available.

Instrument specification and performances in the exam

Candidates bringing in their own instrument must ensure that their keyboard is suitable for the technical requirements of the grade. Electronic keyboards should conform to the following specification: 5 octave keyboard, touch sensitive, keyboard stand, amplification (if required), sustain pedal and all relevant audio and power leads. Keyboards should have a 'realistic' acoustic piano sound which must be used for performance in the exam.

Music Notation Explained

THE MUSICAL STAVE shows pitches and rhythms and is divided by lines into bars. Pitches are named after the first seven letters of the alphabet.

Definitions For Special Piano Notation

Grace Note: Play the grace note on or before the beat depending on the style of music, then move quickly to the note it leads onto.

Spread Chord: Play the chord from the bottom note up, with the top note being reached by the appropriate notated bar position.

Tremolando: Oscillate at speed between marked notes.

Pedal Marking: Depress and then release the sustain pedal.

Glissando: Play the notes before the beat as smoothly as possible.

Finger Markings: These numbers represent your fingers. 1 is the thumb, 2 the index finger and so on.

 (accent) • Accentuate note (play it louder).

 (accent) • Accentuate note with great intensity.

 (staccato) • Shorten time value of note.

 (accent) • Accentuate note with more arm weight.

D.%. al Coda
• Go back to the sign (%), then play until the bar marked *To Coda* ⊕ then skip to the section marked ⊕ *Coda*.

D.C. al Fine
• Go back to the beginning of the song and play until the bar marked *Fine* (end).

Una Corda
• Use damper (soft) pedal

• Repeat bars between signs.

1. **2.**
• When a repeated section has different endings, play the first ending only the first time and the second ending only the second time.

Let's Boogie

Adrian York

When The Saints Go Marching in

Traditional (Arr. John Eacott)

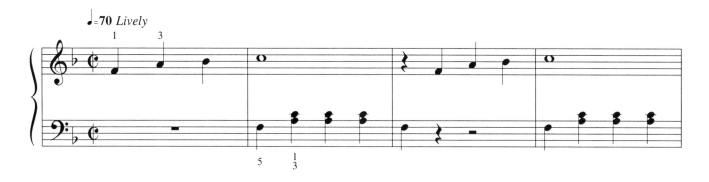

Alone On The Prairie

Nick Ingman

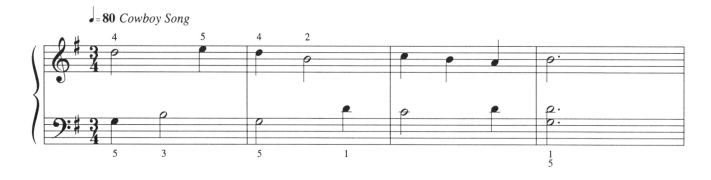

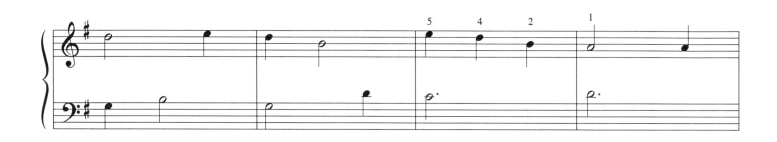

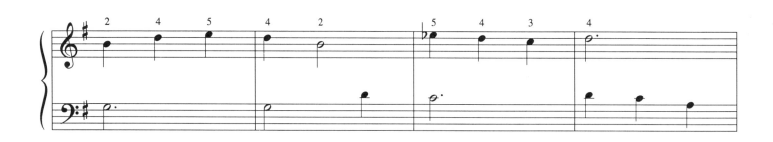

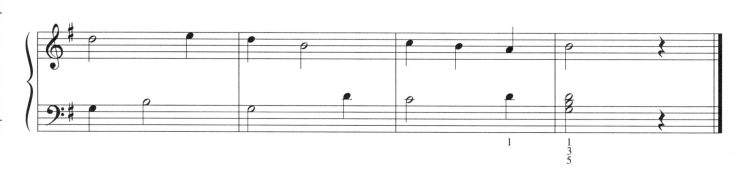

Moving On

Alastair Gavin

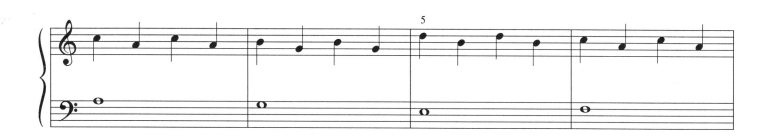

Popular Piano and Keyboards Debut

7

Alouette

Traditional (Arr. Terry Seabrook)

Phantasmaghoulion

Debbie Wiseman

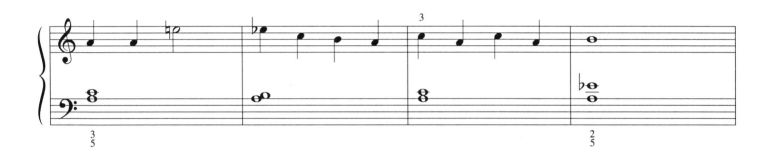

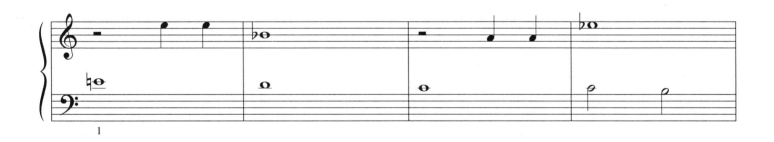

The Guru's Guide To Debut *Popular Piano*

This section contains some handy hints compiled by Rockschool's Popular Piano and Keyboards Guru to help you get the most out of the performance pieces. Do feel free to adapt the tunes to suit your playing style. Remember, these tunes are your chance to show your musical imagination and personality.

Fingerings are suggestions only, so use whichever suit your hands best. Please also note that in tunes with optional solo sections, if the solo option is not taken you should move straight onto the next section.

Popular Piano and Electronic Keyboards Debut Tunes

Rockschool tunes help you play in all the popular piano/keyboard styles you enjoy. The pieces have been written or arranged by top performers and composers according to style specifications drawn up by Rockschool.

Each tune printed here falls into one of six categories: blues, jazz, classic, pop/rock, world and film music. These cover roots, contemporary and global styles that influence every generation of performers.

CD track 1   *Blues*   ***Let's Boogie***

For all you fans of Jools Holland, here's a slice of up tempo boogie woogie that starts to develop the left hand 'rocks' boogie pattern. This tune needs a very solid rhythmic approach and must not be played too politely. Listen to Albert Ammons, Jimmy Yancey and Pete Johnson.

Composer: Adrian York. Adrian is Rockschool's piano syllabus director. He is a successful media composer and a fixture on both the jazz and session circuit who has backed many top artists. Rumour has it that a long time ago he used to play in a well known boy band.

CD track 2   *Jazz*   ***When The Saints Go Marching In***

The Saints is a great vehicle for developing the left hand stride pattern that underpins the Harlem style, a bluesy offspring of ragtime. Make sure you keep the left hand steady and try not to speed up. Watch out for the melody in the left hand in bar 10. Try listening to some Fats Waller to see how the experts do it.

Composer: Traditional (Arr. John Eacott) John worked through the 80's and 90's with artists as diverse as Roman Holliday, Test Department, Loose Tubes and Goldie. He now has a successful career writing music for film, theatre and television as well as researching into 'generative composition'.

CD track 3   *Classic*   ***Alone On The Prairie***

This plaintive song of the lonesome cowboy sets the tone for tunes in later grades that feature the country and western piano style of Floyd Cramer. Watch out for the left hand rhythms as they are not regular and make sure that the E♭ in the right hand doesn't catch you out. Play with a bit of a lilt.

Composer: Nick Ingman. Nick is a freelance composer, arranger and conductor whose work has appeared on 15 No. 1 U.K. hits by Tom Jones, Eric Clapton, Sting, David Bowie, Tina Turner, Paul McCartney and Madonna.

CD track 4   *Pop/Rock*   ***Moving On***

This piece, reminiscent of 70's hard rocks bands like Deep Purple, needs a driving left hand. The crotchets must be kept pumping away until you reach the last four bars where you need to count carefully.

Composer: Alastair Gavin. Alastair has a thriving career as a media composer and is renowned as a fine pianist and keyboardist. He was the keyboard player in the BBC *Rock School* television series in the 1980's and has made appearances with artists as diverse as the Michael Nyman Band, Mari Wilson and trumpeter Harry Beckett.

CD track 5   *World*   ***Alouette***

This is a beautiful arrangement of the classic French folk song with lots going on in both hands to keep you concentrating. Make sure the left hand comes through when it takes over the melody and try to play each phrase in a smooth (legato) and singing manner.

Composer: Traditional (Arr. Terry Seabrook) Terry writes music regularly for television, animated films and adverts. He records and performs with his own Latin group Cubana Bop on the international Jazz and Latin circuit. He also tutors piano as part of the world famous Jamey Aebersold Summer School each year.

CD track 6   *Film*   ***Phantasmaghoulion***

Make sure you count the minim rests fully and take care not to confuse the E and E♭ notes in this tune. It is designed to encourage simple articulation although you might want to try a tremolando on some of the 3 notes chords to make it even spookier!

Composer: Debbie Wiseman. Debbie is one of the U.K.'s top television and film composers. Film scores include *Wilde* and *Tom and Viv*. She has also won prizes for her TV themes for *The Good Guys* and *Shrinks*.

CD Pianist: David Rees-Williams. David has a dual career as a performer and educator. He teaches at Canterbury Christchurch University College and he works internationally as a performer at concerts and festivals, playing everything from baroque harpsichord to jazz piano.

Debut Marking Scheme

The table below shows the marking scheme for the Debut *Popular Piano and Electronic Keyboards* exam.

ELEMENT	PASS	MERIT	DISTINCTION
Piece 1	14 out of 20	16 out of 20	18+ out of 20
Piece 2	14 out of 20	16 out of 20	18+ out of 20
Piece 3	14 out of 20	16 out of 20	18+ out of 20
Piece 4	14 out of 20	16 out of 20	18+ out of 20
Piece 5	14 out of 20	16 out of 20	18+ out of 20
Total Marks	**Pass: 70% +**	**Merit: 80% +**	**Distinction: 90% +**

Entering Rockschool Exams

Entering a Rockschool exam is easy. Please read through these instructions carefully before filling in the exam entry form. Information on current exam fees can be obtained from Rock School by ringing **020 8332 6303**

- You should enter for the exam of your choice when you feel ready.

- You can enter for any one of three examination periods. These are shown below with their closing dates.

PERIOD	DURATION	CLOSING DATE
Period A	1st February to 15th March	1st December
Period B	15th May to 31st July	1st April
Period C	1st November to 15th December	1st October

These dates will apply from 1st January 2001 until further notice

- Please fill in the form giving your name, address and phone number. Please tick the type and level of exam, along with the period and year. Finally, fill in the fee box with the appropriate amount. You should send this form with a cheque or postal order to: **Rockschool, Broomfield House, 10 Broomfield Road, Richmond, Surrey TW9 3HS.**

- Rockschool will allocate your entry to a centre closest to your postcode and you will receive notification of the exam, showing a date, location and time as well as advice of what to bring to the centre.

- You should inform Rockschool of any cancellations or alterations to the schedule as soon as you can as it is not possible to transfer entries from one centre, or one period, to another without the payment of an administration fee.

- Please bring your music book to the exam. You may not use photocopied music, nor the music used by someone else in another exam. The examiner will stamp each book after each session. Performers may be barred from taking an exam if they use music not otherwise belonging to them.

- You should aim to arrive for your Debut *Popular Piano and Electronic Keyboards* exam fifteen minutes before the time stated on the schedule.

- The exam centre will have a waiting area which you may use prior to being called into the main exam room.

- Each Debut *Popular Piano and Electronic Keyboards* exam is scheduled to last for 15 minutes. You can use a small proportion of this time to get ready.

- About 2 to 3 weeks after the exam you will receive a typed copy of the examiner's mark sheet. Every successful player will receive a Rockschool certificate of achievement.

- Rockschool may defer your entry to the next available exam period if the minimum number of candidates for your local centre is not met.

- For all up to date information refer to the Rockschool website **http://www.rockschool.co.uk**.

245 Sandycombe Road
Kew Gardens
Surrey TW9 2EW

t. +44(0)20 8332 6303
f. +44(0)20 8332 6297

info@rockschool.co.uk
www.rockschool.co.uk

IMPORTANT!

<u>Please would you ensure that when completing your examination application form that you advise us of any dates on which you are unavailable.</u>

Exams take place on weekdays, weekends and during school holidays. Prior knowledge of these dates enables the exams to be accurately scheduled minimising the inconvenience caused to both parties by re-scheduling.

We take into consideration any specific requirements and do what we can to meet them whenever possible although this cannot always be guaranteed.

Once an exam has been scheduled it is not always possible to make any alterations.

Thank you for your co-operation.

Rockschool Ltd. Directors: Irma Harrow, Dr Simon Pill, Norton York. Company number: 2610574

Exam Regulations

1. Rockschool exams are open to all persons, irrespective of age and in accordance with our Equal Opportunities policy.

2. Full payment and relevant documentation must reach the offices of Rockschool on or before the chosen exam period's closing date. Rockschool cannot guarantee an exam for any applications received after this date.

3. Exam entries may not be transferred from one candidate to another.

4. Any changes to the examination schedule will incur a fee

5. Cancellation of an exam will result in loss of the exam fee unless as a result of illness or injury. Such cases must be substantiated by a medical certificate. In this event, the exam will be re-scheduled on receipt of half of the original exam entry fee.

6. Names on certificates will be as on the candidate's acknowledgement letter. .Replacement certificates will incur a charge of £5

7. On application, candidates may state times within an exam period when they are unavailable. However, Rockschool cannot guarantee to avoid all such dates.

8. Rockschool reserves the right to defer exams until the next available exam period. After one deferral, an exam is guaranteed at an exam centre chosen by Rockschool. This may not be your local centre.

9. Candidates must use only the official Rockschool sheet music for their respective exam. Photocopying of any material contained within the official published pack is prohibited and may result in disqualification.

10. No refunds are given.

11. No teacher, or other person, must be present during the preparation of a candidate's Quick Study Piece. Any assistance given to a candidate will result in disqualification from the examination.

12. Only the examiner and candidate are allowed to be present in the examination room with the exception of moderators appointed jointly by Rockschool and Trinity Guildhall.

13. Candidates must bring in two copies of music for the 'free choice piece'. Players must use an original copy of the tune to be performed, and must provide a second copy for the examiner, which may be a photocopy. If there is no music available, a zero mark will be given for the piece. Any queries in writing should be addressed to the Director of Operations at least two weeks prior to the exam date.

14. Any backing tracks provided by the candidate for use with 'free choice' pieces must be capable of a music minus 1 playback without the examination part being audible to the examiner. If an unacceptable backing track is submitted, a zero mark will be given for the piece.

15. All band exams are the advertised instruments only. Backing tapes may not be used in the exam.

16. Any special needs candidates must notify the Rockschool office prior to the exam.

17. The examiner's decision is final. Normally, an examiner will hear every component in full, but on occasion an examiner may conclude an examination when a decision has been reached.

18. Replacement certificates may be obtained by successful candidates. All replacements certificates will be marked as such and will incur a charge

19. Rockschool operates a quality assured appeals process. All appeals must be made in writing no later than 14 days after the exam date. There are two criteria for formal appeals, these are:

    * Appeals in respect of errors in procedure

    * Appeals in respect of errors in matching comments to marks awarded.

Full details of Rockschool Ltd's appeal process are available from the Rockschool office

Exclusive Distributors:
Music Sales Ltd
Newmarket Road, Bury St Edmunds
Suffolk IP33 3YB

Published by Rock School Ltd © 2001

Compiled and Edited by Simon Pitt, Adrian York & Norton York
Syllabus manager: Adrian York
Audio producer: Adrian York

Music processing: Simon Troup and Jennie Harrison of Digital Music Art
Cover Design: Bet Ayer

Printed in the United Kingdom by
Caligraving Ltd, Thetford, England

Your Guarantee of Quality

As publishers we strive to produce every book to the highest commercial standards.
The music has been freshly engraved and the book has been carefully designed to minimise
awkward page turns and to make playing from it a real pleasure. Particular care has been
given to specifying acid free, neutral-sized paper made from pulps which have not
been elemental chlorine bleached. This pulp is from farmed sustainable forests,
and produced with special regard for the environment. Throughout, the printing and
binding have been planned to ensure a sturdy, attractive publication which
should give you years of enjoyment. If your copy fails to meet our high standards,
please inform us and we will gladly replace it.

Visit the Rockschool Website at
www.rockschool.co.uk

The full Rockschool publication list can be obtained from
Broomfield House, 10 Broomfield Road,
Richmond, Surrey TW9 3HS

Phone 0208 332 6303
Fax 0208 332 6297

POPULAR PIANO
AND KEYBOARDS   rockschool

➤ **Rockschool** is about playing the styles of music you enjoy. Our specially written tunes develop the key skills, styles and techniques you need so you can play the hits of today, yesterday and tomorrow.

➤ The **Rockschool** packs have standard music notation with recommended fingerings plus great sounding cds recorded live with no digital edits so you can hear how a leading professional performs our tunes. Each **Rockschool** pack has 6 tunes for you to perform by leading British composers and piano players. In this pack these include tunes by **Alastair Gavin**, **Nick Ingman**, and **Debbie Wiseman** amongst others.

➤ This pack contains the tunes from **Debut** in the **Entry Zone**. This is for those of you who are building up confidence in the fundamentals of playing. To help you progress quickly, read our 'Guru's Guide' where you will find hints on playing each tune. There is also a description of all the playing achievements you need to aim for in the **Entry Zone**, both for **Debut** and **Grade 1**, so you can have an overview of your progress at a glance.

➤ Our **Rockschool** grades are accredited by **Trinity College London**. When you take one of our **Rockschool** exams you will have a qualification and measure of your achievement that is recognised around the world. It shows that you can play your music when it really counts.

"There is no doubt that Rockschool is currently the market leader in pop music education"

Times Educational Supplement February 2001

rockschool

Broomfield House,
10 Broomfield Road,
Richmond, Surrey TW9 3HS
Tel: 0208 332 6303
email: office@rockschool.co.uk
internet: www.rockschool.co.uk

Trinity

The International Examinations Board

ISBN 1-902775-26-0

catalogue no. RSK 010101

9 781902 775265